Letterland™

Phonics Practice 2

24 pages

Decodable text

Contains: h, b, f, l, ff, ll, ss, suffix -s /-es, j, v, w, x, y, z, q, Vowels ā, ē, ī, ō, ū ng, suffix -ing

DfE Systematic Synthetic Phonics (SSP) validated

Name:

H h - Harry Hat Man

1. Trace over Harry Hat Man's letter shapes and say his sound.

2. Write over the dotted letters. Then complete the lines.

3. Colour the pictures that start with Harry Hat Man's sound.

4. Write his letter by each object that starts with his sound.

B b - Bouncy Ben

1. Trace over Bouncy Ben's letter shapes and say his sound.

2. Write over the dotted letters. Then complete the lines.

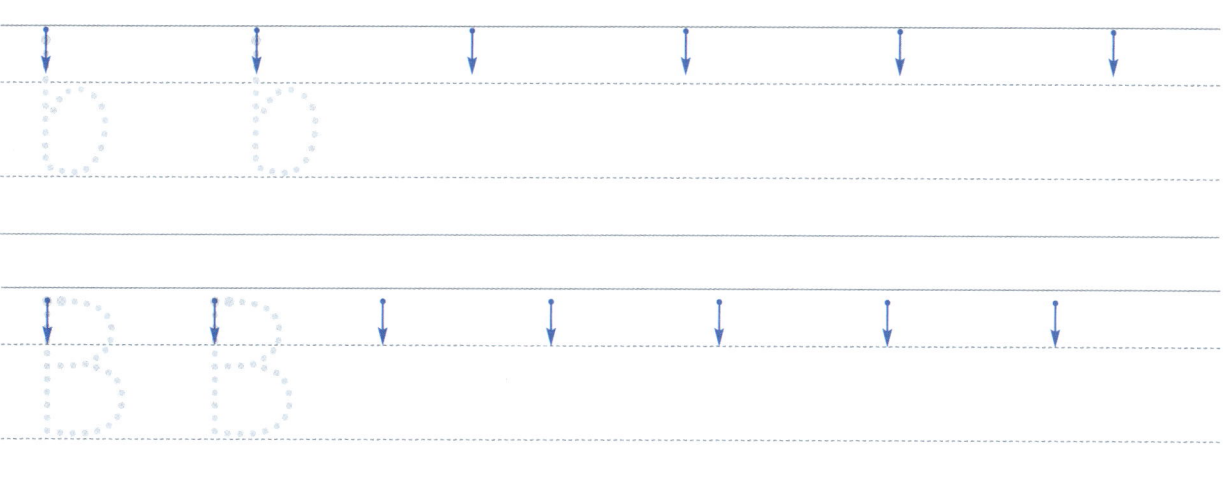

3. Write Bouncy Ben's letter by each object that starts with his sound.

4. Colour the pictures that start with Bouncy Ben's sound.

F f - Firefighter Fred

1. Trace over Firefighter Fred's letter shapes and say his sound.

2. Write over the dotted letters. Then complete the lines.

3. Trace the lines, and then colour the pictures that start with Firefighter Fred's sound.

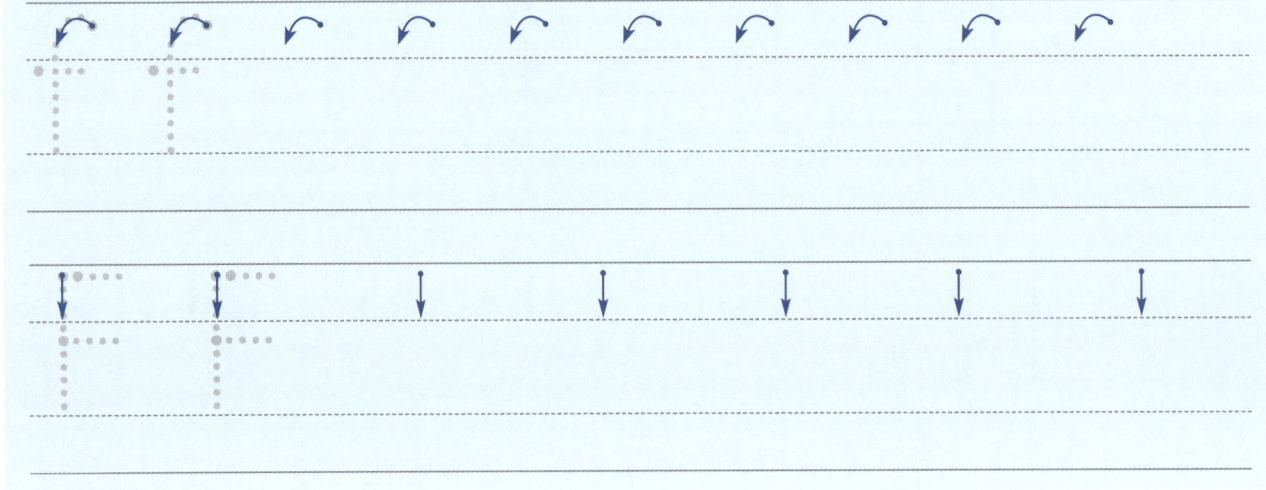

f

4. Write his letter by each object that starts with his sound.

L l - Lucy Lamp Light

1. Trace over Lucy Lamp Light's letter shapes and say her sound.

2. Write over the dotted letters. Then complete the lines.

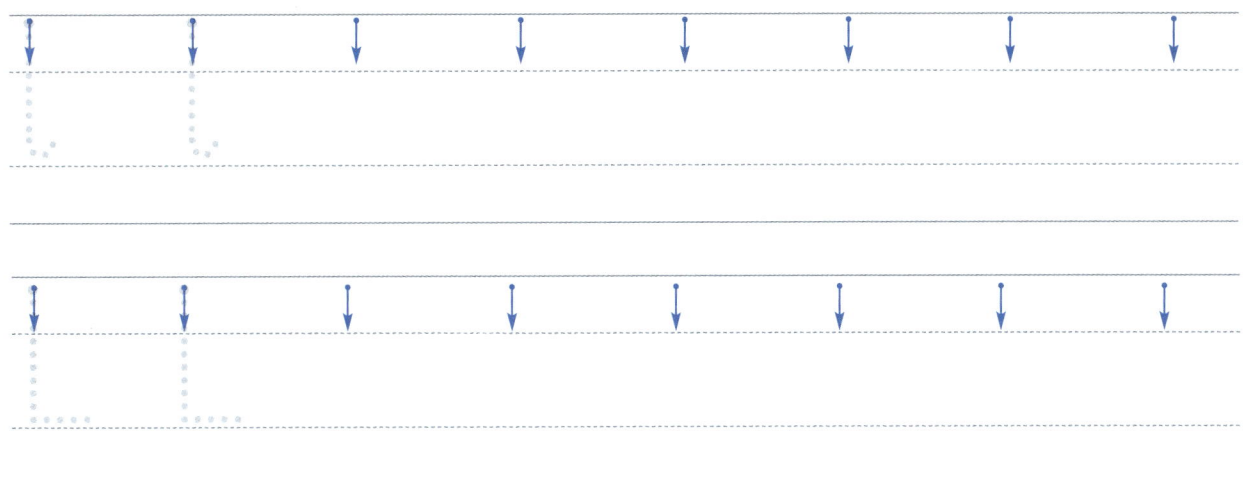

3. Colour the pictures that start with Lucy Lamp Light's sound.

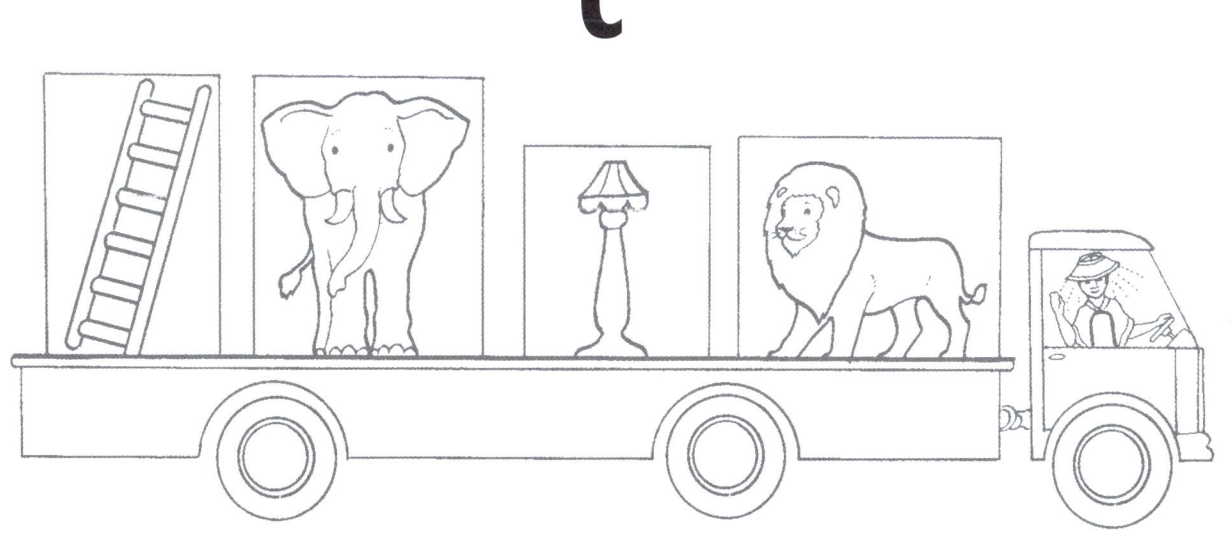

4. Write her letter by each object that starts with her sound.

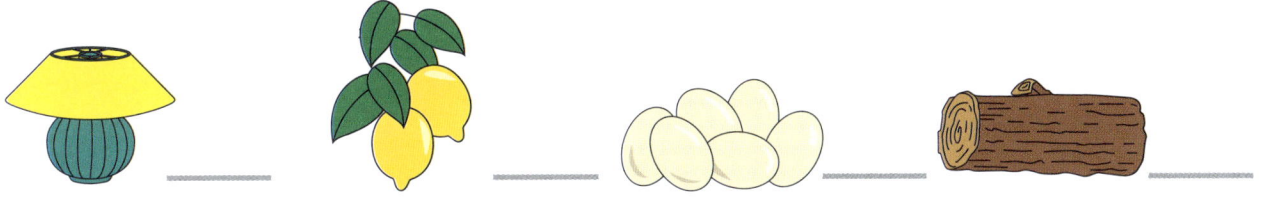

ll as in bell
Best friends on the end

1. Say the words for these pictures.
   Write the words. Circle the best friends at the end.

_____   _____   _____

ff as in puff
Best friends on the end

2. Read this sentence twice.
   Then copy it in the spaces below.

We huff and puff up the hill.

_____   _____   _____   _____

ss as in miss Sammy and Sally Snake

1. Write a short vowel sound in each space to finish each word. Then join the words to the correct pictures.

h__ss

m__ss

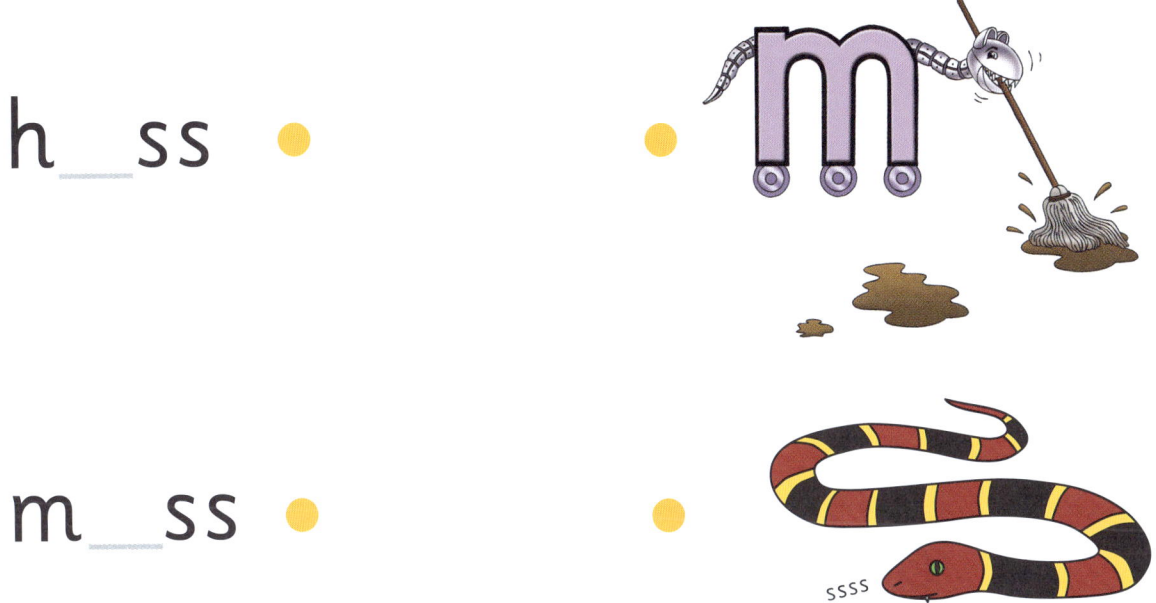

2. Finish writing the last word in each sentence.

It is a ____!

He can ____!

7

Suffix -s

1. Read the sentence. Circle the picture that matches.

Cats on mats.

2. Read the sentence and repeat it. Then copy the missing words on to the lines below.

The cat has lots of dots.

The cat _____ of ____.

Suffix -s/-es

1. Read the number and the word. Add suffix -s or -es to the end.

2 dog ___   4 kiss ___

3 mess ___   5 pet ___

4 hiss ___   3 hat ___

2. Look at these sentences, and try to complete the last word. Read the sentence again.

He _____.

The cat p_____.

J j - Jumping Jim

1. Trace over Jumping Jim's letter shapes and say his sound.

2. Write over the dotted letters. Then complete the lines.

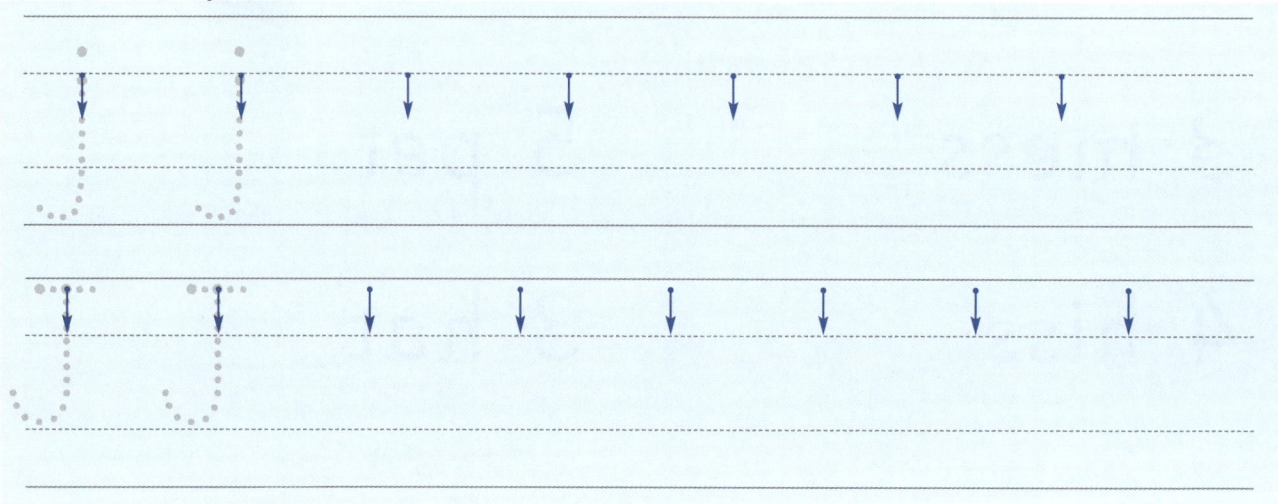

3. Colour the pictures in the jigsaw that start with Jumping Jim's sound.

4. Write his letter by each object that starts with his sound.

V v - Vicky Violet

1. Trace over Vicky Violet's letter shapes and say her sound.

2. Write over the dotted letters. Then complete the lines.

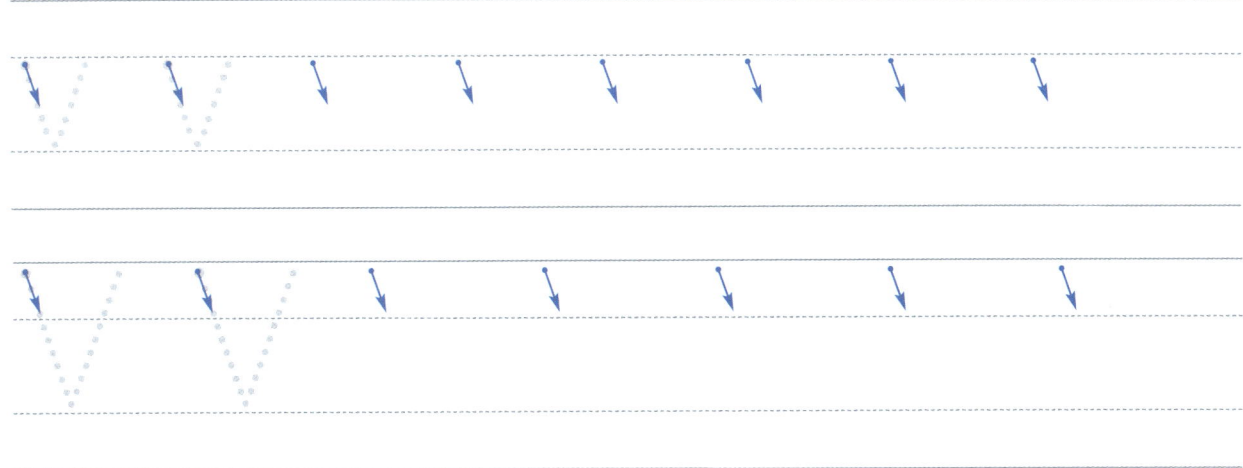

3. Colour the pictures that start with Vicky Violet's sound.

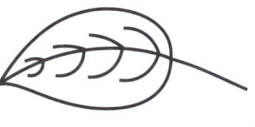

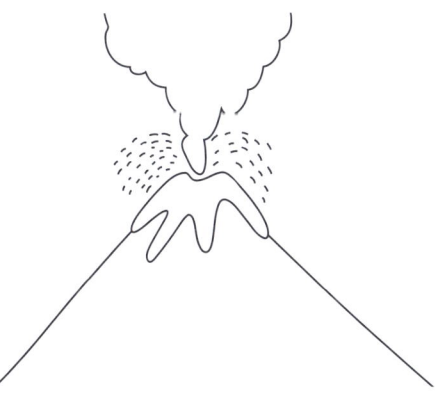

4. Write her letter by each object that starts with her sound.

 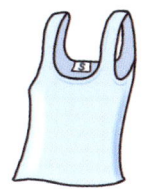 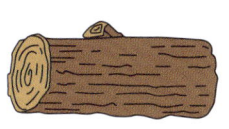 

W w - Walter Walrus

1. Trace over Walter Walrus's letter shapes and say his sound.

2. Write over the dotted letters. Then complete the lines.

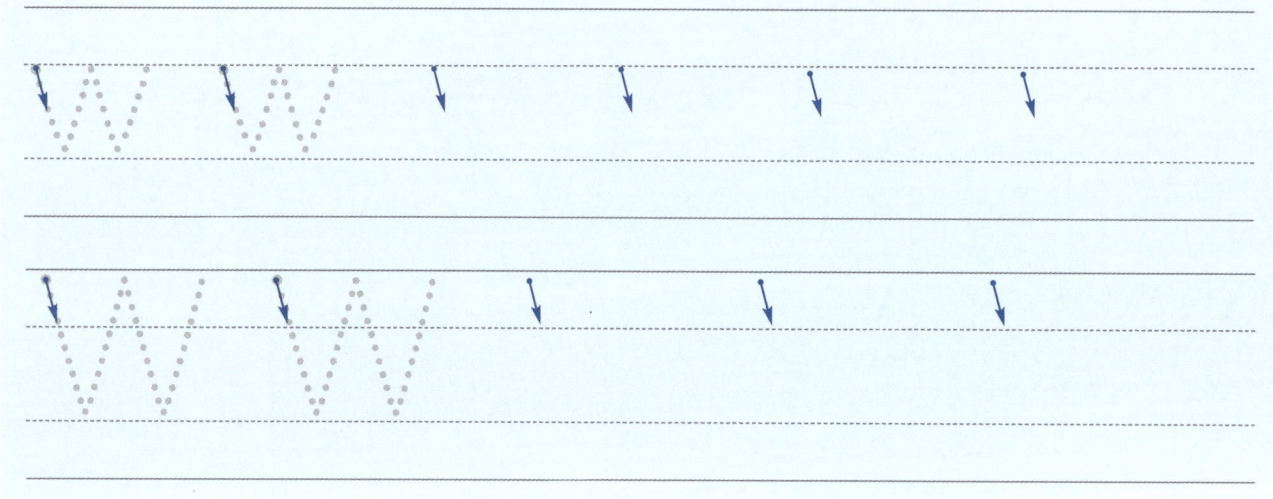

3. Colour the wavy lines that go to pictures starting with Walter Walrus's sound.

4. Write his letter by each object that starts with his sound.

X x - Fix-it Max

1. Trace over Fix-it Max's letter shapes and say his sound.

2. Write over the dotted letters. Then complete the lines.

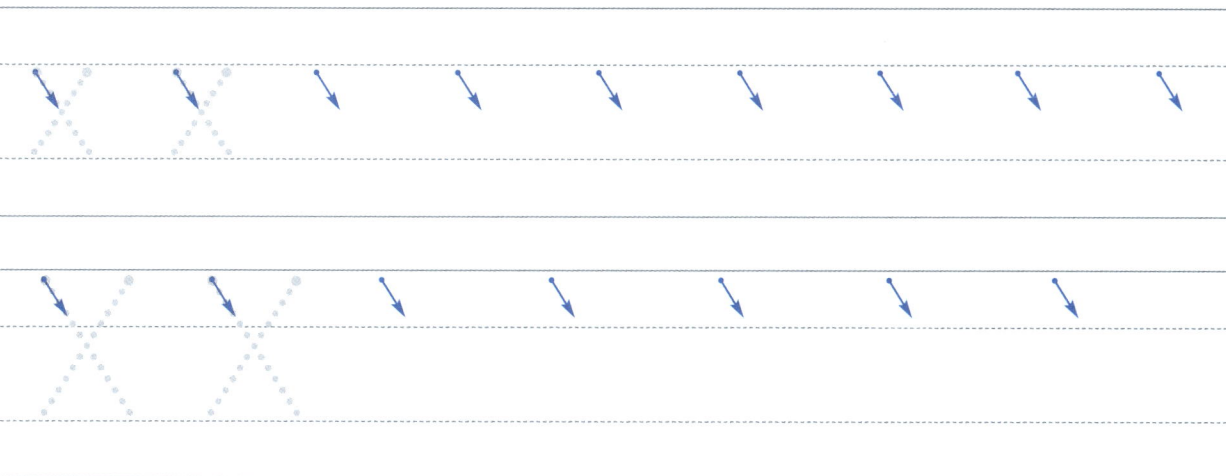

3. Join the pictures that end with Fix-it Max's sound to his letter.

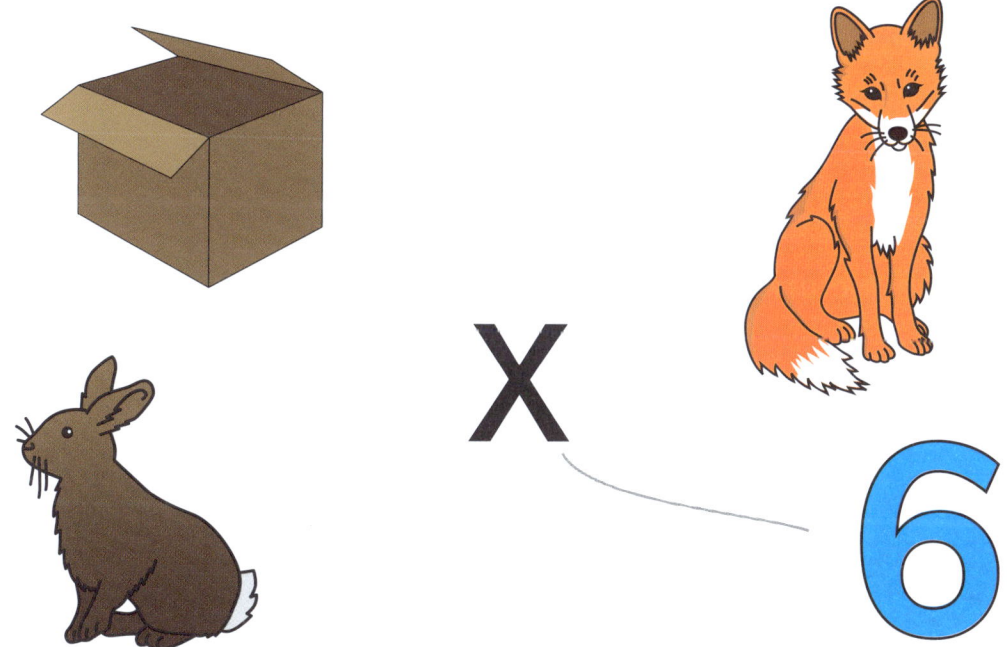

4. Colour the pictures that end with his sound.

   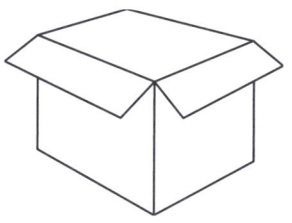

Y y - Yellow Yo-yo Man

1. Trace over Yellow Yo-yo Man's letter shapes and say his sound.

2. Write over the dotted letters. Then complete the lines.

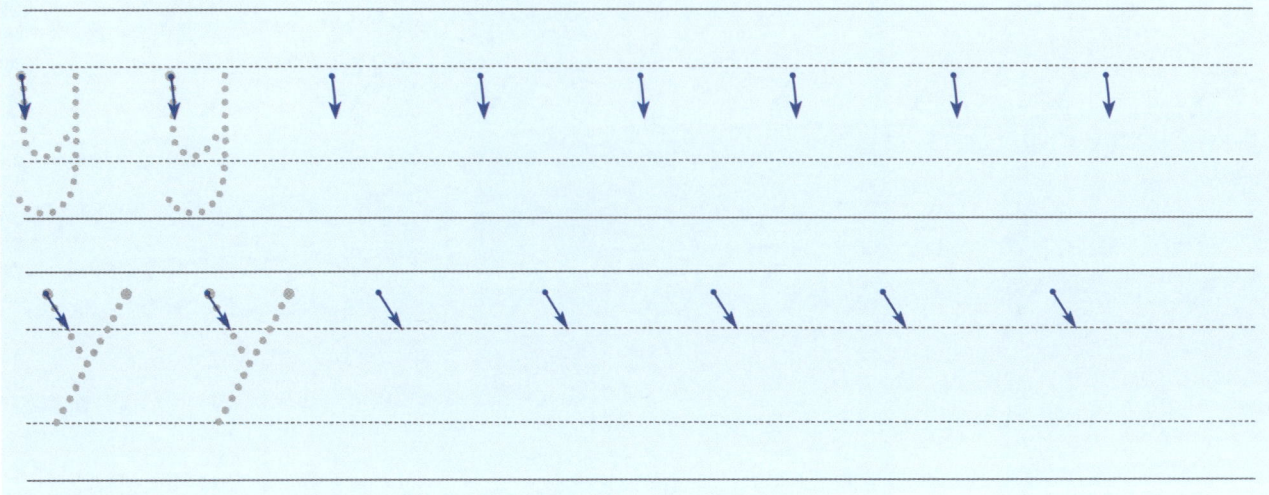

3. Write Yellow Yo-yo Man's letter by each object that starts with his sound.

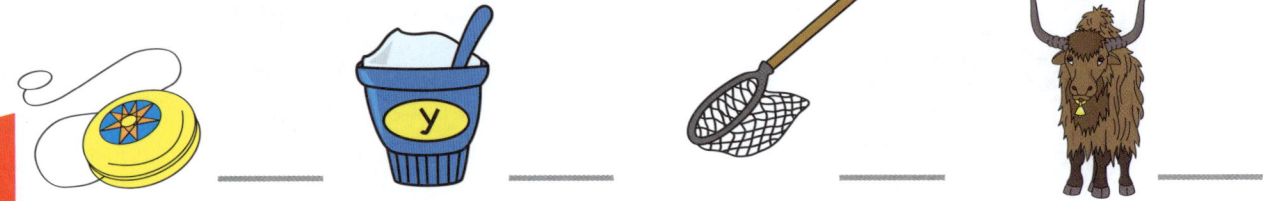

4. Colour the pictures that start with Yellow Yo-yo Man's sound.

14

Z z - Zig Zag Zebra

1. Trace over Zig Zag Zebra's letter shapes and say her sound.

2. Write over the dotted letters. Then complete the lines.

3. Colour the pictures that start with Zig Zag Zebra's sound.

4. Write her letter by each object that starts with her sound.

Q q - Quarrelsome Queen

1. Trace over Quarrelsome Queen's letter shapes and say her sound.

2. Write over the dotted letters. Then complete the lines.

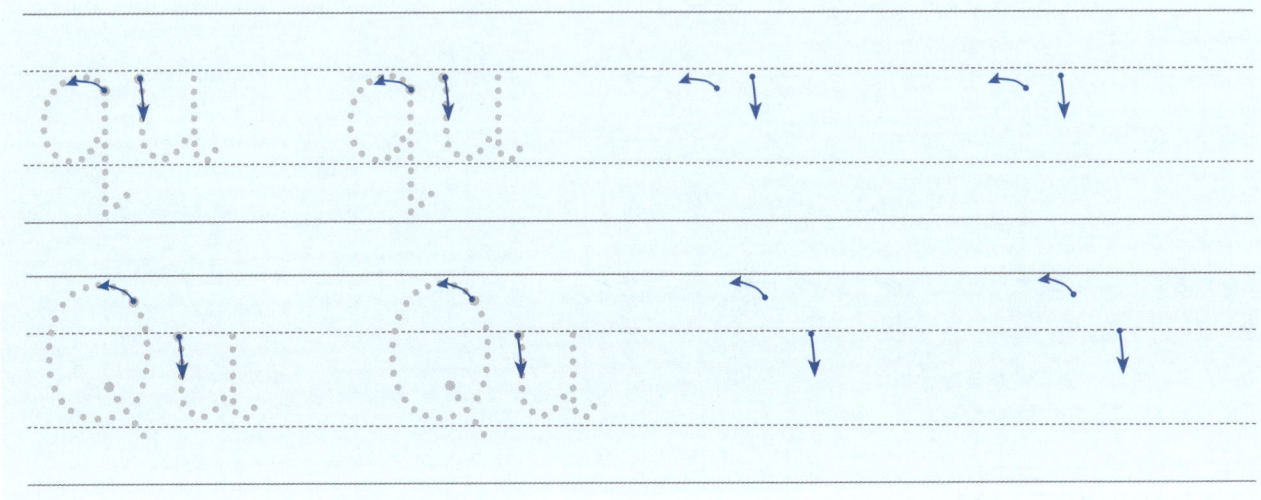

3. Write Quarrelsome Queen's letter by each object that starts with her sound.

4. Colour the pictures that start with Quarrelsome Queen's sound.

Review

1. Write over the dotted letters of the alphabet.

   a b c d e f g h i
   j k l m n o p q r
   s t u v w x y z

2. Look at the pictures and complete the words.

  _ a _    _ a _

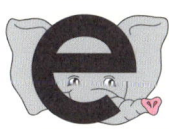  _ e _    _ e _

  _ i _    _ i _

  _ o _    _ o _

  _ u _    _ u _

17

A a - Mr A, the Apron Man

1. Mr A is the Apron Man. Colour the pictures that start with Mr A's name.

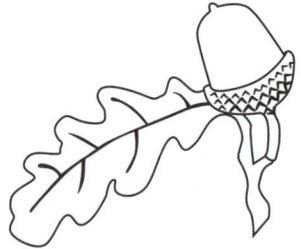
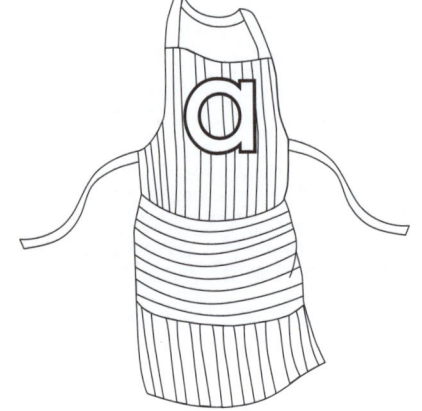

Comparing long and short vowel sounds - ā and ă

1. Draw lines from Annie Apple and from Mr A to the pictures that begin with their sounds.

E e - Mr E, the Easy Magic Man

1. Mr E is the Easy Magic Man. Colour the pictures that start with Mr E's name.

Comparing long and short vowel sounds - ē and ĕ

1. Draw lines from Eddy Elephant and from Mr E to the pictures that begin with their sounds.

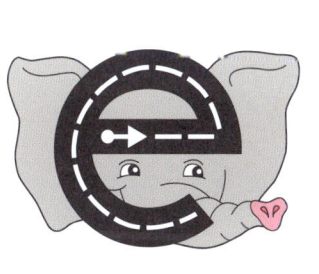

I i - Mr I, the Ice Cream Man

1. Mr I is the Ice Cream Man. Join the pictures that start with Mr I's name to his letter.

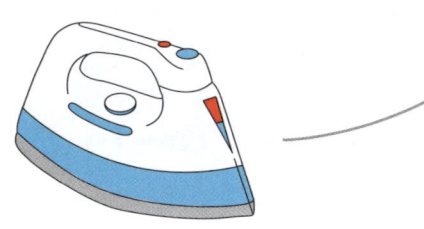

Comparing long and short vowel sounds - ī and ĭ

1. Draw lines from Impy Ink and from Mr I to the pictures that begin with their sounds.

O o - Mr O, the Old Man

1. Mr O is the Old Man. Join the pictures that start with Mr O's name to his letter.

Comparing long and short vowel sounds - ō and ŏ

1. Draw lines from Oscar Orange and from Mr O to the pictures that begin with their sounds.

U u - Mr U, the Uniform Man

1. Mr U is the Uniform Man. Colour the pictures that start with Mr U's name.

u

Comparing long and short vowel sounds - ū and ŭ

1. Draw lines from Uppy Umbrella and from Mr U to the pictures that begin with their sounds.

ng as in ring Noisy Nick and Golden Girl

1. Read the words. Join them to the picture that matches.

sing

hang

ring

ding dong

Suffix -ing

1. Read each sentence. Write the suffix **ing** to complete each word. Then join the sentence to the correct picture.

A sock is miss_____.

The king is kiss_____.

How to use this book

On each page, read the instructions to the children. Name all the pictures with them. Let them try and read all the words in the exercises themselves, as they are decodable.

Letter sounds
Many of the activities in this book rely on knowing the **a-z** letter sounds. Make sure children use the Letterland Sound Trick to discover the letter's sound:

Just START to say any Letterlander's name, and catch the very first sound that comes out of your mouth. That sound is actually the sound that letter makes in words.
For example: Bouncy Ben 'b...' (not 'buh' or 'bee'), Eddy Elephant 'eh...' (not 'ee'), Firefighter Fred 'fff...' (not 'fuh' or 'ef')

Letter shapes
By making sure children start with the right movement pathway for each letter, you will be ensuring that on moving to joined-up handwriting the transition will be smooth and easy. If young children are allowed to form letters their own way, incorrect habits quickly become deep-rooted and can be very difficult to correct later.

Upper/lowercase pairs
Ask the children to look carefully at the differences in the size and shape of each upper/lowercase letter pair. The need to make this judgement for themselves prepares them for writing without lines.

It is important to use this workbook:
- when children are not tired
- when there are no background distractions
- for short periods of time
- with plenty of praise and encouragement.

Left-hander

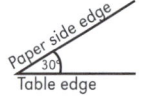
Fingertips 4cm from tip of pencil
Paper side edge / Table edge
Elbows off the table
Feet on floor

Right-hander
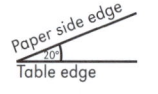

Paper side edge / Table edge
Chair slightly tilted
Feet on floor
Fingertips 2cm from tip of pencil

Published by Letterland International Ltd.
8/10 South Street, Epsom, Surrey, KT18 7PF, UK
© Letterland International 2021
10 9 8 7 6 5 4 3 2

ISBN: 978-1-78248-553-7
Product Code: TP66

LETTERLAND™ is a trademark of Letterland International Ltd.
Printed in China.

All rights reserved. No part of this publication may be reproduced, stored in a retrieval system, or transmitted in any form or by any means, electronic, mechanical, photocopying, recording or otherwise, without the prior permission of the Publisher or a licence permitting restricted copying in the United Kingdom issued by the Copyright Licensing Agency Ltd, 90 Tottenham Court Road, London W1P 0LP. British Library Cataloguing in Publication Data. A catalogue record for this book is available from the British Library.

Sassoon Infant is a typeface designed for children learning to read and write.
© Adrian Williams Design Ltd

Written and designed by Lisa Holt
Consultant: Lyn Wendon, originator of Letterland

You may also like:
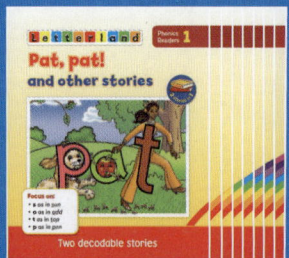
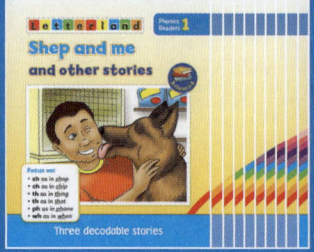

See our full range at: www.letterland.com

Please Note: These practice books match the teaching order in the Letterland *Phonics Teacher's Guide*.

For those who wish to follow a different teaching order the practice books can be used flexibly.

Code: TP66
ISBN 978-1-78248-553-7
Letterland Child-friendly phonics